ANNUAL
2018

PaRragon

Bath · New York · Cologne · Melbourne · Delhi
Hong Kong · Shenzhen · Singapore

Contents

Meet Team Bob!

ROLEY

LOFTY

Grab your tool belt and hard hat! It's time to join Bob the Builder and his team, as they fix things in Fixham and help construct Spring City. No project is too big or too small – whether it's mending a leaky roof or repairing a skyscraper. After all, the fun is in getting it done!

With his trusted partner, Wendy, keen apprentice builder, Leo, and a team of helpful machines, Bob digs into any project and hammers out a solution with a smile on his face!

TINY

MUCK

WENDY   **BOB**

LEO

DIZZY

SCOOP

TWO-TONNE

CAN THEY FIX IT?
YES, THEY CAN!

Bob the Builder

Bob is a busy builder who lives in Fixham and works in Spring City. There's no job too big or too small that Bob and his team can't handle!

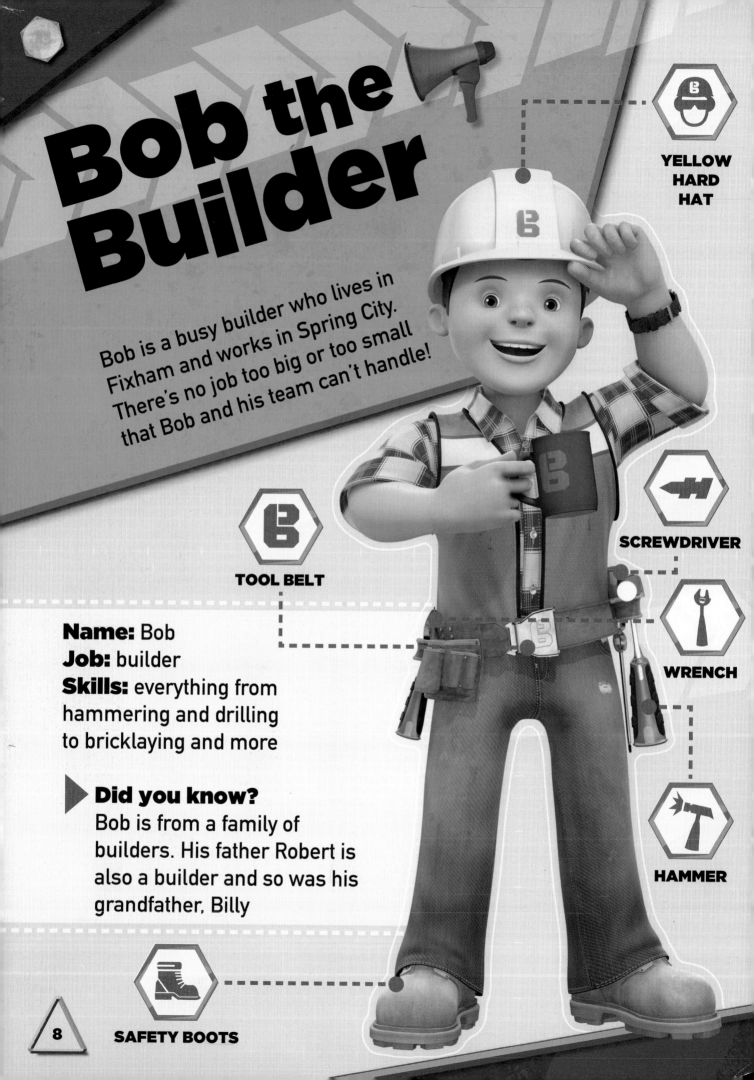

YELLOW HARD HAT

SCREWDRIVER

WRENCH

HAMMER

TOOL BELT

Name: Bob
Job: builder
Skills: everything from hammering and drilling to bricklaying and more

▶ **Did you know?**
Bob is from a family of builders. His father Robert is also a builder and so was his grandfather, Billy

SAFETY BOOTS

Guide Bob through the maze to Spring City, collecting Wendy and Leo on the way.

START

FINISH

"CAN WE FIX IT?"

Answer on page 68

9

Wendy

Meet Wendy, Bob's super smart building partner. Wendy is good at all sorts of building jobs, but her favourite thing to fix is anything electrical.

"DON'T WORRY, TEAM!"

BLUE HARD HAT

VEST

MULTI-METER

PLIERS

WIRE STRIPPERS

SAFETY BOOTS

Name: Wendy
Job: builder and electrician
Skills: electrics, sanding, painting and more

▶ **Did you know?**
Wendy looks after the team's tools and keeps them in tip-top condition

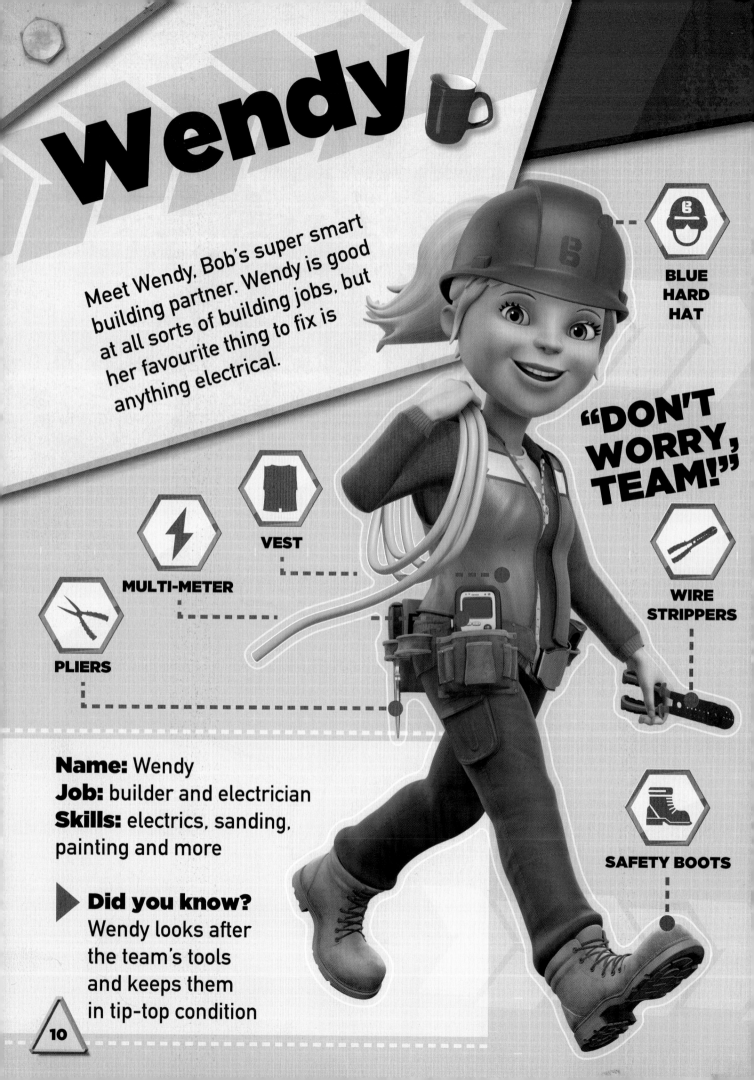

Leo

Leo is keen to learn, although he can be a bit clumsy! He wants to be just like his hero, Bob, one day.

WHITE HARD HAT

SCREWDRIVER

VEST

WRENCH

"WHAT'S GOING ON?"

TOOL BELT

Name: Leo
Job: apprentice builder
Skills: fetching and carrying, doing small jobs

▶ **Did you know?**
Leo's dad Curtis runs the garage in Fixham

Super Scoop

Scoop the yellow digger is a super scooper! He has a bucket at the front and a trench digger at the back, which can be changed to a useful drill.

ORANGE LIGHT

EXHAUST PIPE

BUCKET

CAB

ALL-WEATHER TYRES

Name: Scoop
Machine: digger
Skills: digging and carrying, being a leader

▶ **Did you know?**
Scoop is scared of heights, and likes to keep his wheels firmly on the ground

Can you circle all five differences between these pictures of Scoop and Bob?

1

2

Large Lofty

Lofty is a large mobile crane with a big imagination. The trouble is, the more Lofty thinks, the more this shy crane worries that things will go wrong!

"IT'S A JOB WELL DONE!"

JIB

CAB

CHASSIS

HOOK

STEEL CABLES

Name: Lofty
Machine: mobile crane
Skills: lifting and moving big and heavy materials, demolition

▶ **Did you know?**
Lofty uses a wrecking ball for demolition jobs

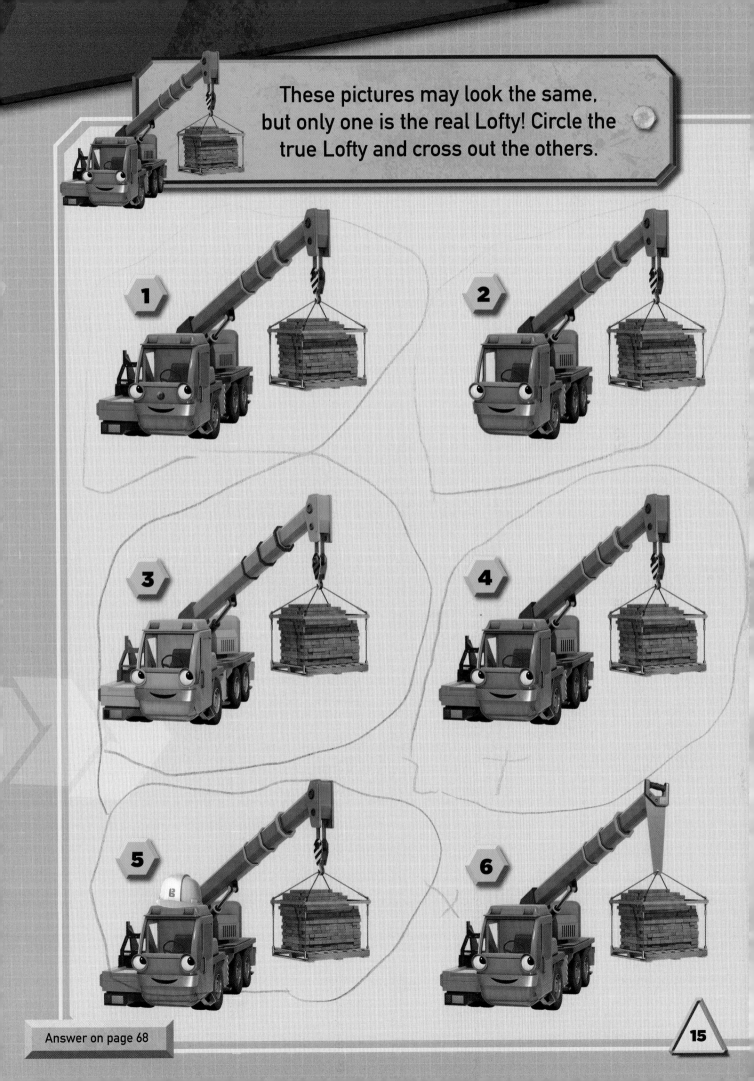

These pictures may look the same, but only one is the real Lofty! Circle the true Lofty and cross out the others.

1

2

3

4

5

6

Messy Muck

Muck is a digger-dumper who gets excited about everything – especially digging and dumping! Wherever there's mud, messy Muck rolls right in!

CAB

DUMPER

BUCKET

CATERPILLAR TRACKS

Name: Muck
Machine: digger-dumper
Skills: digging trenches, clearing dirt and rubble, moving heavy loads

▶ **Did you know?**
Muck loves squelchy mud and splashing through puddles!

"I'D LOVE TO JOIN IN!"

16

Draw lines to match the pictures of Muck to the correct jobs.

1

lifting

2

bulldozing

3

tipping

Busy Dizzy

Dizzy is a clever little cement mixer. Sometimes she is so keen to help that she does things without thinking – and often ends up in a real spin!

Draw lines to match the words to the different views of Dizzy.

front   **back**   **side**

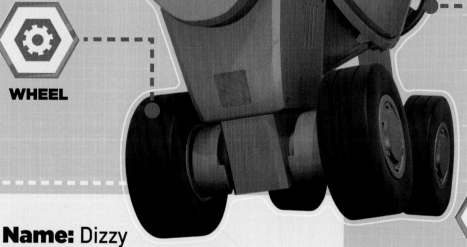

CONTROLS

WHEEL

MIXING DRUM

HANDLE

Name: Dizzy
Machine: portable cement mixer
Skills: mixing cement

▶ **Did you know?**
Dizzy can mix cement on the move

"POUR TO PERFECTION!"

Answers on page 68

Rolling Roley

Roley is a green machine who likes to stay clean, which can be a problem on a building site! He might not be the fastest worker, but Roley rolls perfect roads... with no bumps!

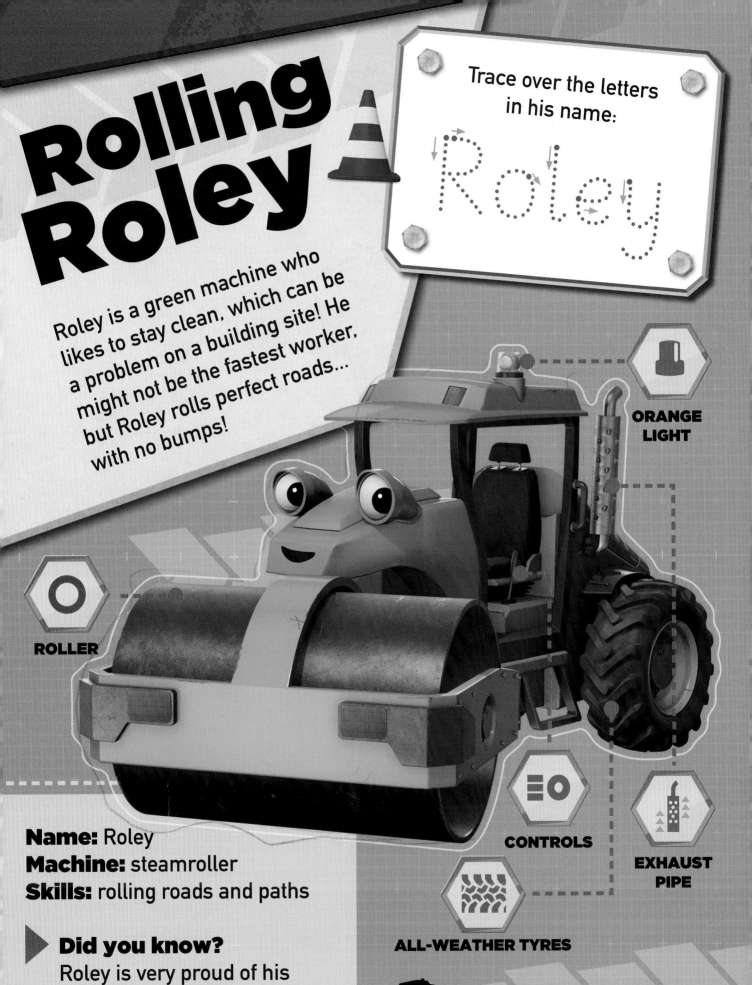

ORANGE LIGHT

ROLLER

CONTROLS

EXHAUST PIPE

ALL-WEATHER TYRES

Name: Roley
Machine: steamroller
Skills: rolling roads and paths

▶ **Did you know?**
Roley is very proud of his perfect green paintwork

"THE TARMAC IS FLAT!"

19

Towering Tiny

The only thing that's tiny about this crane is his name! Towering Tiny stands tall above Spring City. He uses his tower power to lift the biggest and heaviest loads.

Find these close-ups in the big picture of Tiny.

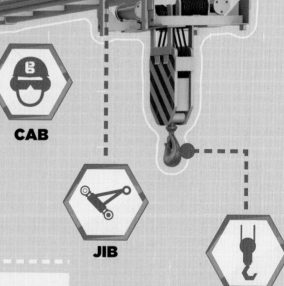

CAB

MAST

JIB

HOOK

Name: Tiny
Machine: crane
Skills: lifting loads of all shapes and sizes

▶ **Did you know?**
Tiny is tall and tough, but he's a gentle giant

"TIME FOR SOME TOWER POWER!"

Answers on page 68

Tough Two-Tonne

Two-Tonne is an HGV who likes to get everything just right. He can haul all sorts of heavy things on his trailer and can mix cement too.

Find five spanners hidden in the picture.

LIGHTS

HUGE WHEELS

INDICATORS

EXHAUST PIPE

Name: Two-Tonne
Machine: heavy goods vehicle (HGV)
Skills: transporting big and heavy things, mixing cement, tipping loads

▶ **Did you know?**
Two-Tonne is strong enough to shift Bob's mobile office

"I'LL DO IT THE RIGHT WAY!"

Answers on page 68

21

Messy mix-up!

Accidents happen, especially when Leo is around! Draw lines to help him tidy the paint pots and brushes into pairs. Circle the object that is not part of a pair.

Answers on page 68

Who's calling?

Bob can contact his friends on his tablet wherever he is working. Which letter does each friend's name start with? Say the letter sound out loud and then trace over the dotted letters.

Wendy

Leo

Tilly

Jenny

Mayor Madison

Curtis

Bob the Brave

Bob and the team had an important job at Fixham Castle. Mayor Madison needed help to get the castle ready for Fixham Festival.

"OK, team," said Bob. "Today we're building a **portcullis**!"

"Now, does anyone know what a portcullis is?" asked Wendy.

But none of the machines did.

Just then, Leo piped up. "It's a like a big gate that can be lifted up and down. It was used in olden times to keep people out."

"That's exactly right, Leo!" smiled Bob.

Bob stepped onto the castle's wooden drawbridge, and noticed a big hole. The wood was rotten! "Hmm, we'll have to repair the drawbridge," he said.

Bob told the machines to stay where they were – Lofty, Muck and Scoop were too heavy to cross the rotten drawbridge.

"We'll make a new drawbridge before tonight's festival," said Bob.

"First we've got a portcullis to fix," added Wendy.

"That's right. **Can we build it?**" asked Bob.

"Yes, we can!" the team replied.

Everyone set to work.

Bob **hammered**, Wendy **measured**, Leo **sawed** and Lofty **lifted**.

Bob told the team all about castles. "Kings and queens lived in castles. Their children were princes and princesses, who were like young royal apprentices."

"Kind of like you, Leo!" said Lofty.

Leo grinned. "Brave Prince Fix-a-Lot! And his three knights in shining metal – Sir Scoop, Sir Muck and Sir Lofty!"

"Hurrah!" cheered the machines.

Suddenly, Leo tripped over his toolbox, and landed with a **thump**.

"Up you get, your majesty," laughed Wendy. "Let's try raising the portcullis."

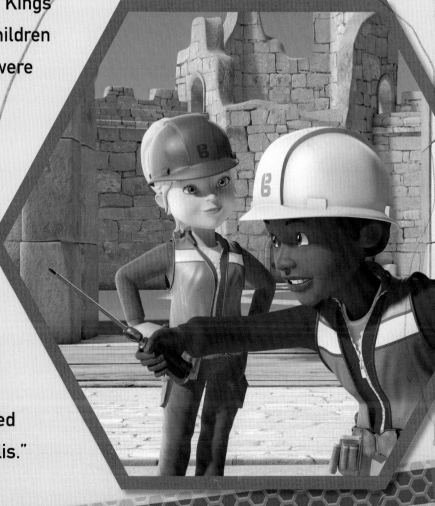

Leo and Wendy took their places, either side of the castle wall. But, when a seagull swooped close to him, Leo let go of the winch. The portcullis came crashing down, **CLANK!**

"Fear not, everyone! Prince Fix-a-Lot will fix this!" Leo called from inside the castle.

But when he tried to turn the winch, it wouldn't budge.

"The portcullis is too **heavy**!" said Bob. "Sit tight, Leo. We'll get you out somehow."

"Bob, if we can't raise the portcullis," Wendy worried, "there won't be a Fixham Festival!"

Leo looked around to find another way out of the castle. "Another adventure for fearless Prince Fix-a-Lot," he grinned.

But in the castle courtyard Leo heard a strange moaning noise.

"Wooah-oowooaa!"

"What was that?" cried Leo, running to hide behind a wall.

Leo didn't know that the noise was just Mr Bentley, practising his singing for the festival!

"What's wrong, Leo?" Lofty called.

"I think it's a **g-g-ghost**!" Leo shivered.

"Don't be silly, Leo!" Lofty laughed. "There are no such things as **ghosts** ... are there, Bob?"

"Of course not!" Bob chuckled.

Bob had to get inside the castle to help Leo, but the castle walls were much too high to climb. Then, he had a clever idea.

"If this works, we'll be able to open the portcullis and rescue Leo," he smiled. "But it will take **courage**, **determination** and a dollop of **axle grease**! **Can we save Leo?"**

"Yes, we can!" Wendy and the machines replied.

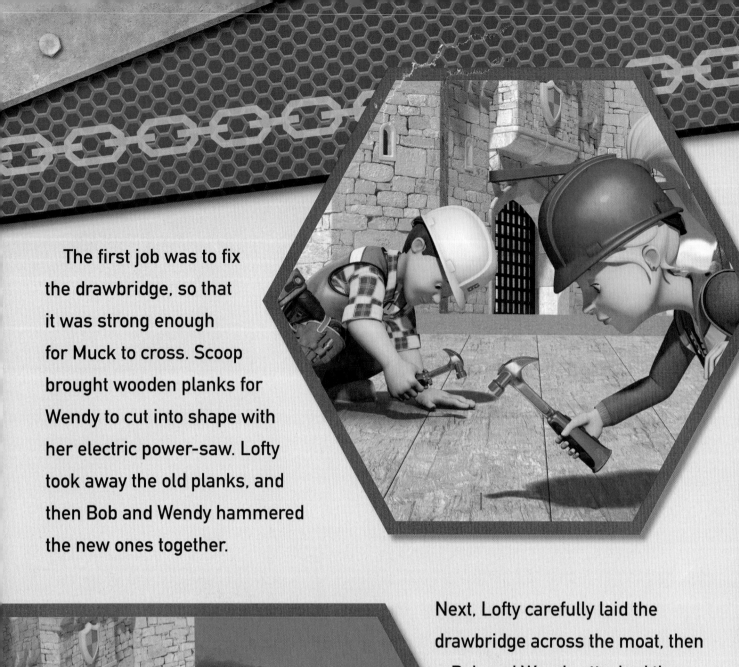

The first job was to fix the drawbridge, so that it was strong enough for Muck to cross. Scoop brought wooden planks for Wendy to cut into shape with her electric power-saw. Lofty took away the old planks, and then Bob and Wendy hammered the new ones together.

Next, Lofty carefully laid the drawbridge across the moat, then Bob and Wendy attached the chains. The new drawbridge was ready!

"OK, Muck. Lift the portcullis as high as you can," said Bob.

Muck dug his bucket and raised the portcullis just high enough so that Bob could roll underneath. The heavy portcullis crashed down seconds later.

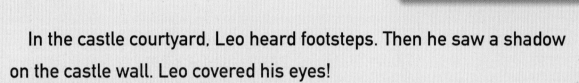

In the castle courtyard, Leo heard footsteps. Then he saw a shadow on the castle wall. Leo covered his eyes!

"W-who's there?" Leo whispered.

"Hello, your majesty," said a familiar voice.

"Bob? Oh! **My hero**!" Leo sighed happily.

Then came the strange moaning noise again. **"Wooaah . . . ooaah!"**

Leo leapt up onto a nearby bench ... as Mr Bentley stepped out from a doorway!

"You look like you've seen a **ghost**, Leo," said Mr Bentley. "I didn't startle you with my fabulous singing, did I?"

"Of course not," Leo pretended. He tried to get down from the bench, but his foot was stuck!

Bob unscrewed the bench and soon freed Leo's foot. "There you go, Prince Fix-a-Lot!" Bob laughed.

"Thanks – **a lot**!" Leo smiled.

Moments later, Bob and Leo raised the portcullis together.
Wendy and the machines clapped and cheered, as Bob, Leo and
Mr Bentley crossed the drawbridge.

"Well done, team!" Wendy smiled.

"The castle is ready for the festival!" Bob added.

"That reminds me," said Mr Bentley. "I must collect the costume that
Mayor Madison ordered for me." And he dashed away, wondering what
he would be dressed as – a noble **king**? A **knight** in shining armour?

That night, the castle was lit up with
spotlights. It looked magnificent! When the
drawbridge opened and the portcullis
went up, Mr Bentley appeared ...

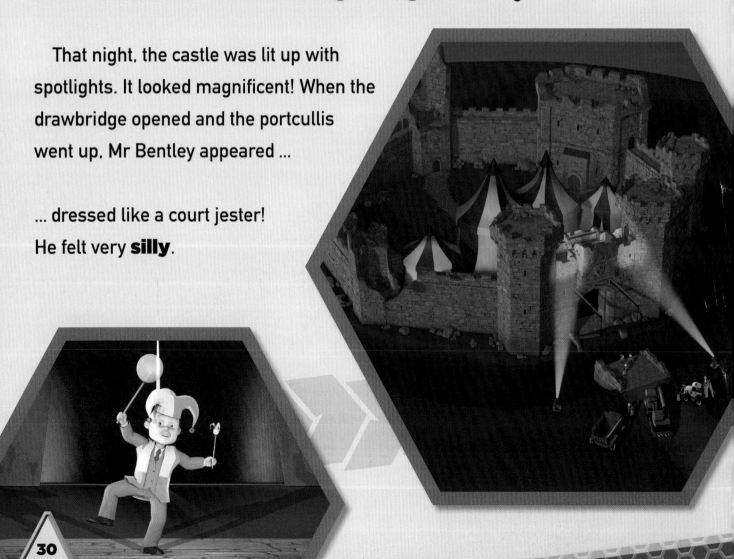

... dressed like a court jester!
He felt very **silly**.

"Welcome, gentlefolk of ye olde Fixham Town!" Mr Bentley announced. "All hail Queen Madison."

"For your rescue efforts, and making my castle look glorious, I knight you, **Bob the Brave**," said the Mayor, placing a wooden sword on Bob's shoulders. "I thank your team of valiant vehicles," she went on.

"Hurrah!" cheered the machines, clanking their metal parts loudly.

And that night, everyone enjoyed a Fixham Festival that was fit for royalty!

The End

Fixham Festival

Mayor Madison needs the team's help to get Fixham Castle ready for the festival. Lead the brave crew to the castle as quickly as you can.

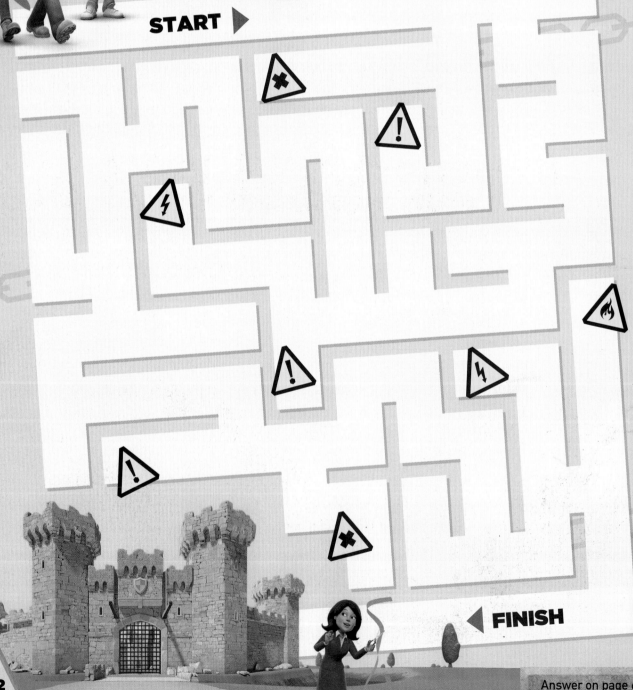

START ▶

◀ **FINISH**

Answer on page 68

Building's a breeze!

Bob and his team make building look easy! Can you spot five differences between these two pictures of Bob, Wendy and Leo?

Colour a breeze block each time you spot a difference.

1

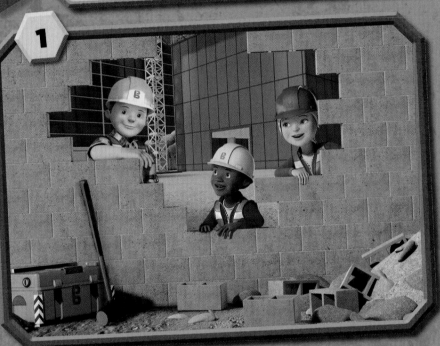

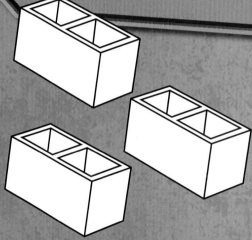

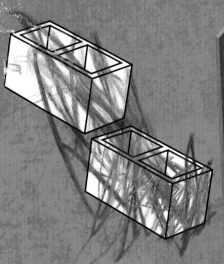

2

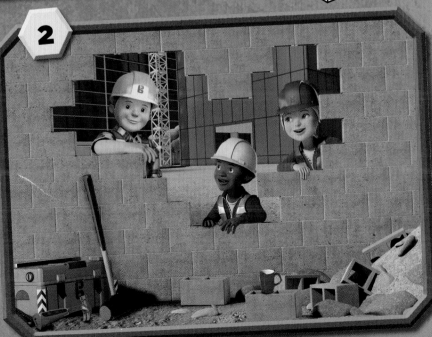

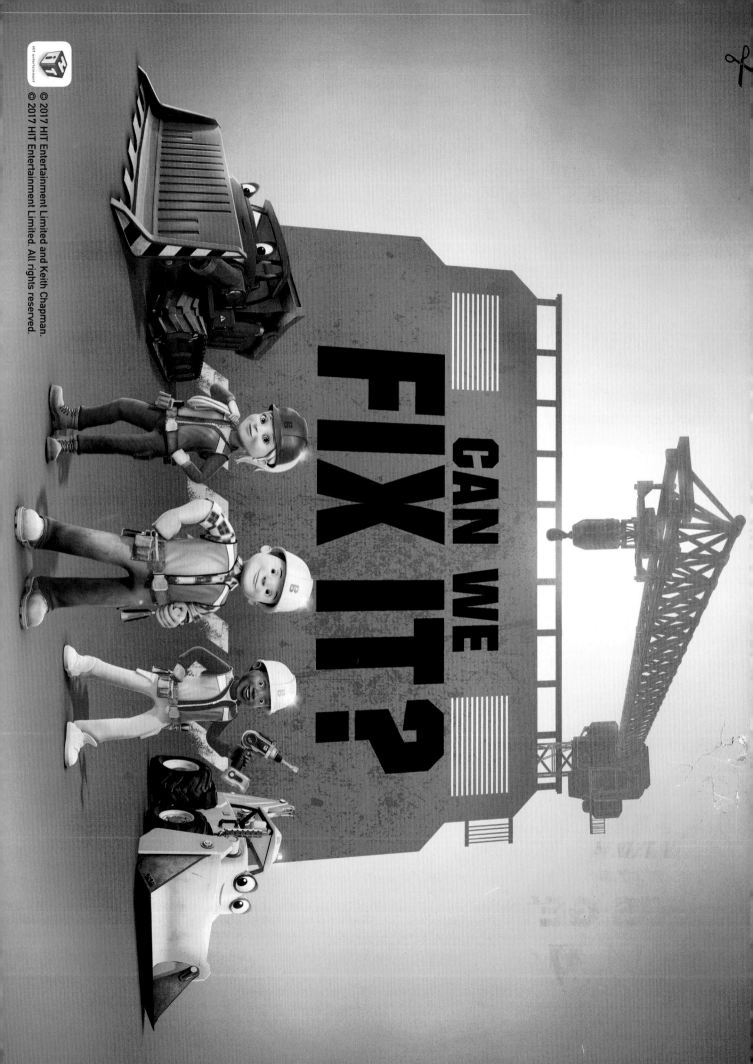

LET'S GET BUILDING

Tool trouble

Bob and his crew need all sorts of tools to get the job done. Draw the tool that is missing from each pattern.

Answers on page 69

Vet visit

Starting at number 1, join the dots to reveal who's visiting vet Tilly today.

whose job?

Help Bob match the machines to the jobs they do best. One machine doesn't have a job. Can you circle the picture?

rolling

mixing

moving dirt

drilling

lifting

Answers on page 69

Brilliant Betsy

Betsy takes the Rockets wherever they want to go in Spring City. Colour in Betsy using the little picture as a guide. **Beep! Beep!**

Make a Bob mask!

Ask an adult to help you make this Bob mask, perfect to wear on or off site. **Can you make it? Yes, you can!**

Make your mask

1 Draw a straight line to divide your plate into two halves.

2 Colour or paint the top half yellow and the bottom half pink.

3 Cut two small card circles for Bob's ears and glue them in place. Paint these pink, too.

4

When the mask has dried, draw three black lines on Bob's hat, then two eyes, a nose and mouth and Bob's brown hair.

5

Cut out the B for Bob and stick it in place on his hard hat.

6

Ask an adult to cut out two eyeholes.

7

Cut two lengths of string or elastic and make a knot in one end of each length.

8

Ask an adult to make two side holes with a pencil, as shown. Thread the elastic through the side holes and put on your mask. Tie the elastic behind your head tightly enough so it doesn't slip down.

Rub-a-dub Roley

Roley has time for a quick wash before the next big build. Which two pieces are missing from the picture?

a

b

c

d

Answers on page 69

Ready to roll

a

b

c

d

43

Milkshake mix-up

Bob and the team were busy getting Chef Tattie's Milkshake Bar ready for its grand opening.

"The building is finished, next we have to build the car park and finish off a few things inside," Bob smiled.

Scoop looked up at the giant milkshake on the roof of the building.

"It's **spectacular**!" said Lofty.

Just then, Wendy arrived. Her job was to put a motor inside the milkshake, to make it spin round.

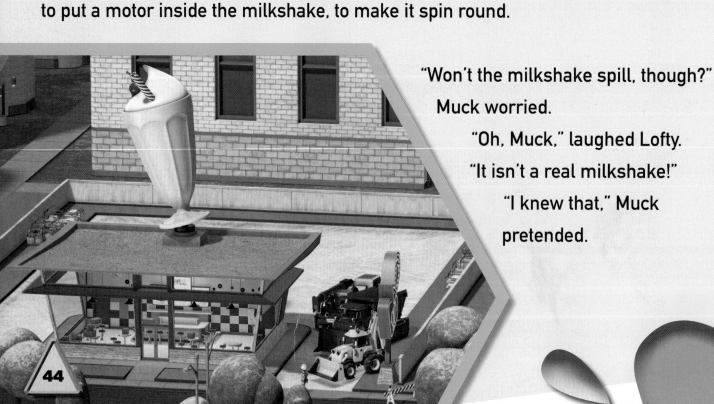

"Won't the milkshake spill, though?" Muck worried.

"Oh, Muck," laughed Lofty. "It isn't a real milkshake!"

"I knew that," Muck pretended.

"Chef Tattie's Milkshake Bar is going to be such a **fun** place!" Scoop smiled.

"It really is," said Chef Tattie, who appeared carrying a box of fruit.

Bob was puzzled. "What are you doing here, Chef?" he said. "We haven't finished."

"I know," said Chef Tattie. "But while you're hard at work, I'll be creating my special **Tattie-licious Shake-tastic Surprise!**"

"What's in it?" asked Scoop.

"I've no idea," the chef replied. "I just love experimenting with new ingredients. I mix them all up and see what comes out!"

Scoop was amazed.

"OK, team, let's get started," said Bob. "Muck, you'll be laying the aggregate. Lofty, you'll be shifting materials and Scoop, you'll be mixing the concrete for the car park with Two-Tonne.

So, **can we build it?"**
"Yes, we can!"
the machines replied.

Bob and the team set to work. Wendy was on the roof, fixing the motor to the model milkshake, while Bob was inside, tiling the walls. Muck was collecting stones for the car park and Lofty was fetching the ingredients for Two-Tonne's concrete.

Soon, Two-Tonne pulled up with his cement-mixer trailer.

Scoop rushed up to greet him. "Hey, Two-Tonne," he began. "The Milkshake Bar is going to be such a fun place. So I thought we could do something **fun** with the concrete too!"

The big truck looked puzzled.

"We could mix up some **new** ingredients and see what comes out. That's what Chef Tattie does," Scoop went on.

"Oh, no," Two-Tonne said. "You don't mess with concrete. We'll make our usual concrete – flat, smooth and very grey."

Inside the Milkshake Bar, Chef Tattie had been busy creating lots of different shakes.

"Who will try my marvellous milkshake creations?" he asked.

Bob and Wendy couldn't wait to taste the yummy shakes!

Muck and Scoop rolled up to watch through the window. Whizzing up fruit, splashing in milk, Chef Tattie was putting on a real show.

"I wanted to make some **fun** concrete for Chef Tattie," Scoop told Muck. "But Two-Tonne will only make **normal** concrete."

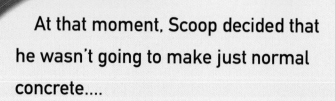

At that moment, Scoop decided that he wasn't going to make just normal concrete....

"Today, I'll be mixing up my **Scoop-ilicious Concrete-tastic Surprise**!" he said.

"But what will Two-Tonne say?" gasped Muck.

"Two-Tonne doesn't have to know," Scoop smiled.

Two-Tonne told Scoop exactly how to make the concrete. "Remember, Scoop," he said. "Always measure out the ingredients, or it just won't work. It's two parts cement, two parts aggregate, one part water, one part sand ..."

"Got it!" Scoop smiled, giving Muck a wink.

Before Muck could stop him, Scoop had **scooped** up a pile of wood chippings and **tipped** them into Two-Tonne's mixing drum. Next, Scoop knocked over a rubbish bin – and tipped the yucky contents into the drum too!

"Am I ready to go, Scoop?"
Two-Tonne asked.

"Yes, Two-Tonne," Scoop smiled.
"Now let's mix it up!"

When the concrete was ready,
Two-Tonne carefully poured it out, to make
the surface for the car park. Then he rolled
away. It had been a busy day!

The next morning, Scoop brought Bob to
see his special **Scoop-ilicious** concrete.

"Wow! My concrete looks amazing,"
Scoop smiled. "It's so **fun**, and, er ...
squelchy!" he gasped, as his wheels sank
into the sticky grey sludge.

"Scoop!" said Bob. "This concrete's
not set!"

"It's the **strangest**
concrete I've ever seen,"
added Lofty, picking up an
old banana skin with his jib.

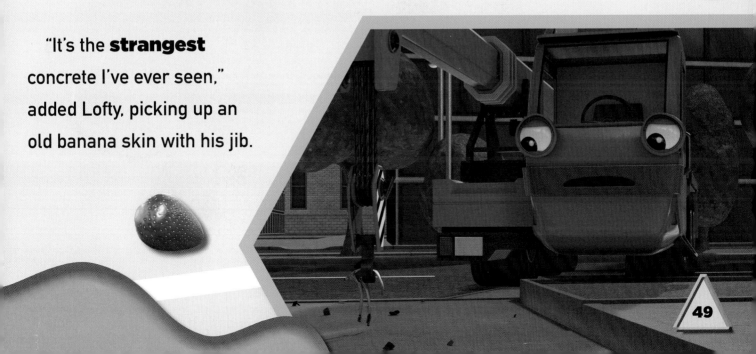

Scoop felt sad.
"Anyone can make a mistake," Bob said kindly.

"But I did it on purpose," Scoop replied. "When I saw Chef Tattie mixing different colours and ingredients, it looked like so much fun," Scoop explained. "I wanted to try something fun too. I'm sorry, Bob."

Bob walked away without a word. Scoop thought that Bob was cross, but he came back a little later, with Muck, Dizzy and some colourful sacks of cement.

"Right, Scoop," smiled Bob. "I want you to try again using some fun ingredients ... that don't come out of the **dustbin**!"

The machines got to work. Dizzy mixed up the new cements, one by one, and Scoop tipped out load after colourful load for Muck to flatten and finish the car park.

"This looks loads better than the last **mess** you made, Scoop," Muck teased.

"Thanks, Muck!" Scoop smiled.

Inside the Milkshake Bar, Chef Tattie handed Bob and Wendy a pink milkshake with two straws.

"Here it is," Chef Tattie said proudly. "My **Tattie-licious Shake-tastic Surprise!**"

"Delicious!" smiled Bob, slurping the yummy shake. "What flavour is it?"

"It's just plain strawberry," Chef Tattie smiled. "Because sometimes normal is best!"

The End

Make a milkshake

Try Chef Tattie's recipe to make your own super-scrummy milkshake! The recipe will make two tasty shakes.

Ask an adult to help you chop and blend your shake!

You will need:

- 100g strawberries
- 1 small banana
- 1 tsp strawberry jam
- 150ml cold semi-skimmed milk, soya milk or other milk alternative

How to make:

1 Remove the hulls from the strawberries and chop the fruit in half. Save two strawberries for later.

2 Next, peel the banana and chop into slices.

3 Put the chopped fruit and the jam in a blender with a splash of milk, and whizz up until smooth.

4 Keeping adding milk until you have a shake with just the right thickness.

5 Serve in tall glasses with a straw, and a strawberry each to decorate.

Hats on!

Before beginning any build, Bob and the team put on their hard hats. Follow the lines to match Bob, Leo and Wendy to their hats.

a

b

c

54

Answers on page 69

Join the team!

Bob needs an apprentice to help him with his next project – will you join the team? Colour your own hard hat using your favourite colours.

Construction quiz

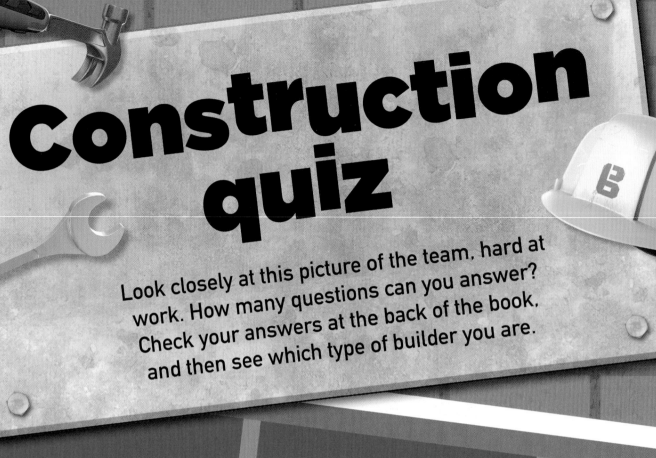

Look closely at this picture of the team, hard at work. How many questions can you answer? Check your answers at the back of the book, and then see which type of builder you are.

1. What colour is Wendy's toolbox?

☐, ☐ or ☐?

2. Is Leo **pushing** ☐ or **pulling** ☐ some equipment?

3. Is Bob **hammering** ☐, **drilling** ☐ or **digging** ☐?

4. How many piles of bricks can you count?

3 ☐, 4 ☐ or 5 ☐?

How did you score?

1 correct answer: Apprentice builder
You're keen, but still have lots to learn. Pay attention, work hard, and you'll be a master builder one day!

2 or 3 correct answers: Building partner
You work hard and are a brilliant member of the team. Remember, think big: build big!

4 correct answers: Master builder
Born to build, you always know the right tools to get the job done. Can you build it? Yes, you can!

Making tracks

Make way for the machines! Follow each machine's trail with your finger or a pencil without touching the sides.

START

START

59

Cone count

Lofty and Leo are laying out cones, but they keep losing count!

Help Lofty and Leo!
Count the cones, and then colour the numbers.

How many cones are **blue**?

2 3 4

How many cones are **orange**?

3 4 5

How many cones are **green**?

5 6 7

How many cones have been **knocked over**?

1 2 3

Answers on page 69

Trusty tools

Leo is helping Bob sort the tools in his toolbox. Read the story out loud. Every time you see a picture, say the word.

hard hat   **boots**   **tool belt**   **Bob**

Leo   **Mayor Madison**   **paint pots**   **rollers**   **mug of tea**

Every day, 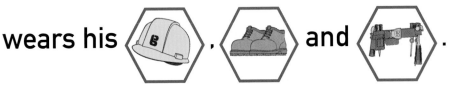 makes sure he has the right tools for

the job, so that he can work quickly and safely. He always

wears his ⬡ , ⬡ and ⬡ .

One day, ⬡ and ⬡ were helping ⬡ .

They had to build her a new desk and paint her office.

carried in some and  to do the

painting, while brought his screwdriver, some

screws and his trusty hammer.

 and worked hard together until the jobs

were done. The mayor's office looked perfect! "There's

just one more thing a good builder needs," said to

 . went to fetch his toolbox.

"You won't find it in there!" chuckled.

looked puzzled as left the office. Then

came back a couple of minutes later, carrying a hot

 for and a for himself.

"Cheers!" said . "A is something a good

builder can't do without – even if it won't fit in a toolbox!"

Tool tidy

Bob takes good care of his tools. Draw lines to match each tool to its shadow. What is the name of the tool that doesn't have a shadow?

The tool without a shadow is:

....

Answer on page 69

My toolbox

Here is a toolbox of your own! Draw and colour some tools, just like Bob's. Great work!

Ready for lift-off!

Lofty and the team are helping launch a rocket! Spot the close-ups from the panel below in the big picture.

Answers on page 69

Busy Bob

Phew! After all that building,
Bob has earned a tea break.
Colour in Bob using the
smaller picture to help you.

Answers

page 9:

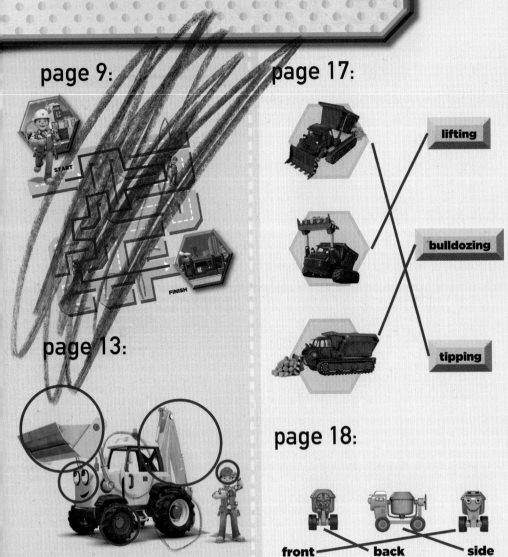

START

FINISH

page 13:

page 15:

page 17:

lifting

bulldozing

tipping

page 18:

front   back   side

page 20:

page 21:

page 22:

page 32:

START ▶

◀ FINISH

page 33:

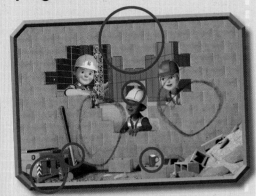

page 36:

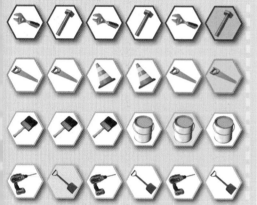

page 37:

Cooper is visiting the vet.

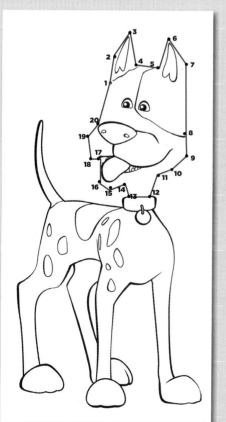

page 39:

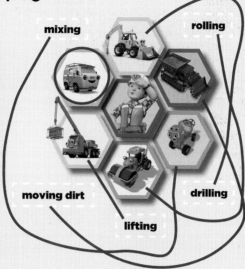

page 42:

Pieces a and b were missing.

page 43:

Pieces b and d were missing.

page 54:

page 57:

1. yellow
2. pulling
3. drilling
4. 3

page 61:

There are 4 blue cones.
There are 5 orange cones.
There are 6 green cones.
2 cones have been
knocked over.

page 64:

saw

page 66: